New school clothes

The ACE project

'Literacy for Active Citizenship' series

Written by Valona Renner-Thomas
Illustrated by Diana Galloway

New school clothes
© Learning Unlimited 2015

Published by Learning Unlimited Ltd as part of the Active Citizenship and English (ACE) project. The ACE project, led by Learning Unlimited, was funded through the European Integration Fund and delivered in partnership with Blackfriars Settlement, Working Men's College and the UCL Institute of Education.

Foreword

The ACE project
'Literacy for Active Citizenship' series

The Active Citizenship and English (ACE) project, led by Learning Unlimited and delivered in partnership with Blackfriars Settlement, Working Men's College and the UCL Institute of Education, received funding from the European Integration Fund (July 2013 to June 2015).

The ACE project aimed to support non-EU women to develop their skills and confidence in English and to take an active part in everyday life in the UK. As part of the project we wanted to produce a series of readers for our learners, and other adults also settling in the UK, which include stories about funny, personal and less typical aspects of everyday life in the UK. These stories were written by learners and volunteer befrienders on the ACE project and edited by ESOL specialists at Learning Unlimited. The supporting activities were also developed by the Learning Unlimited team.

We hope you enjoy using the 'Literacy for Active Citizenship' series.

To find out more about the ACE project, please see:
www.learningunlimited.co/projects/ace

My name is Rosila and I come from Sierra Leone. I have a six year old daughter called Mabinti. We recently came to England to join my husband.

He has found a new school for Mabinti in our area and it does not have a uniform.

The weather in England is very cold so I took Mabinti shopping for warm clothes.

We went to Peckham market because it was nearby. There were lots of bargains and very colourful clothes.

Mabinti really liked a fluffy pink coat and a pink flannel top with matching trousers. They were warm and pretty. We thought they were perfect for school so I bought them for her.

The next morning Mabinti woke up early because she was so excited about her first day at school. She got dressed in her lovely pink clothes and we set off early.

As we left our flat we met our friendly next door neighbour. "You look nice and warm, Mabinti," she said. "Where are you going?"

We told her that it was Mabinti's first day at school.

"Oh! But you can't wear those clothes to school," she said. "They are night clothes."

She said that the pink fluffy coat was a dressing gown. The matching trousers and top were pyjamas – sleeping clothes!

We told her that in our village in Sierra Leone people wear their old clothes to bed. We didn't know about dressing gowns and pyjamas!

The kind neighbour took us shopping to buy some different clothes for school. We bought a scarf, a hat and a pair of gloves too. They were very warm but not as nice and colourful as the nightwear!

Later we told our story to our family in Sierra Leone. We all laughed a lot – clothes just for sleeping in!

Now I am an expert in buying warm winter clothes. I can help other people to choose winter clothes in the UK that are not pyjamas!

Key words

excited	feeling happy
expert	someone who knows a lot about something. For example, Jamie Oliver is an expert at cooking.
gloves	clothes to wear on your hands
market	an outside shopping place
neighbour	the person who lives next door to you
pyjamas	trousers and top to sleep in
scarf	a long piece of material to keep your neck warm
uniform	special clothes children wear for school

Questions

1. Why did Mabinti and her mother go shopping?

2. What did they buy in Peckham market?

3. What did the neighbour say to Mabinti and her mother?

4. What do people in their village wear to go to bed?

5. If someone from the UK went to your country, would they need to buy different clothes?

6. When you arrived in the UK, did you have to buy new clothes? Who helped you to choose them?

7. Describe the uniform you wore to school or the uniform your child wears.

Activity 1

Role play

Work in groups of three or four people.
Choose a role to play:

- Mabinti

- Rosila

- A market trader selling clothes

- The neighbour

- A friend

Act out some parts of the story:

- Mabinti and Rosila choosing clothes
  at the market stall

- Mabinti, Rosila and the neighbour

- Mabinti, Rosila and a friend

Activity 2

Write a letter or email to a friend back home.

Either

Describe what you do to keep warm in the winter in the UK.

Or

Describe some of the things people wear which you find surprising or shocking, such as green and pink hair!

For more downloadable activities, visit:
www.learningunlimited.co/resources/publications

Acknowledgements

New school clothes was written by Valona Renner-Thomas and illustrated by Diana Galloway. We are grateful to them for being able to include their work as part of the 'Literacy for Active Citizenship' series.